Real Science-4-

Level I

Laboratory Workbook

Rebecca W. Keller, Ph.D.

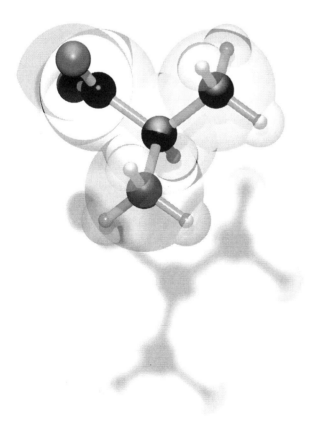

Cover design: David Keller
Opening page: David Keller, Rebecca W. Keller, Ph.D.
Illustrations: Rebecca W. Keller, Ph.D.

Real Science-4-Kids: Chemistry Level I-Laboratory Workbook

ISBN 10: 09749149-1-6 (Previously ISBN # 1-931796-02-5)
ISBN 13: 9780974914916

Published by Gravitas Publications, Inc.
4116 Jackie Road SE, Suite 101
Rio Rancho, NM 87124
www.gravitaspublications.com

Printed in the United States

Gravitas
Publications Inc.

Keeping a Laboratory Notebook

A laboratory notebook is essential for the experimental scientist. In this type of notebook, the results of all the experiments are kept together along with comments and any additional information that is gathered. For this curriculum, you should use this workbook as your laboratory notebook and record your experimental observations and conclusions directly on its pages, just as a real scientist would.

The experimental section for each chapter is pre-written. The exact format of a notebook may vary among scientists, but all experiments written in a laboratory notebook have certain essential parts. For each experiment, a descriptive but short Title is written at the top of the page along with the Date the experiment is performed. Below the title, an Objective and a Hypothesis are written. The objective is a short statement that tells something about why you are doing the experiment, and the hypothesis states the predicted outcome. Next, a Materials List is written. The materials should be gathered before the experiment is started.

Following the Materials List, the Experiment is written. The sequence of steps for the experiment is written beforehand, and any changes should be noted during the experiment. All of the details of the experiment are written in this section. All information that might be of some importance is included. For example, if you are to measure 1 cup of water for an experiment, but you actually measured 1 1/4 cup, this should be recorded. It is sometimes hard to predict the way in which even small variations in an experiment will affect the outcome, and it is easier to track a problem if all of the information is recorded.

The next section is the Results section. Here you record your experimental observations. It is extremely important that you be honest about what is observed. For example, if the experiment instructions say that a solution will turn yellow, but your solution turned blue, you must record blue. You may have done the experiment incorrectly, or you might have discovered a new and interesting result, but either way, it is very important that your observations be honestly recorded.

Finally, the Conclusions should be written. Here you will explain what the observations may mean. You should try to write only valid conclusions. It is important to learn to think about what the data actually show and what cannot be concluded from the experiment.

Laboratory Safety

Most of these experiments use household items. However, some items, such as iodine, are extremely poisonous. Extra care should be taken while working with all chemicals in this series of experiments. The following are some general laboratory precautions that should be applied to the home laboratory:

Never put things in your mouth without explicit instructions to do so. This means that food items should not be eaten unless tasting or eating is part of the experiment.

Use safety glasses while working with glass objects or strong chemicals such as bleach.

Wash hands before and after handling chemicals.

Use adult supervision while working with iodine and while conducting any step requiring a stove.

Contents

Experiment 1: What is it made of?   Date: _____

Objective   To become familiar with the periodic table of elements and investigate the composition of some common items

Materials

pen
paper
food labels
dictionary
encyclopedia
periodic table of elements

Experiment

Record your answers on the next page.

❶ Using the periodic table of elements, answer the following questions:

A. How many protons does aluminum have? How many electrons?

B. What is the symbol for carbon?

C. List all of the elements that have chemical properties similar to helium.

D. What is the atomic weight for nitrogen? How many neutrons does nitrogen have?

❷ Think of several different items and write them in the column labeled "Item." These can be any item, like "tires" or "cereal." Try to be specific. For example, instead of writing just "cereal," write "corn cereal" or "sweet, colored cereal."

❸ In an encyclopedia or on the food label, look up the composition of the items you have selected, and write this information in the column labeled "Composition." Try to be as specific as possible when identifying the composition. For example, if your cereal contains vitamin C, write "sodium ascorbate" if that name is also listed. Try to identify any elements in the compounds you have listed. For example, vitamin C contains the element "sodium."

❹ Write the source next to the composition. "Source" means where you got your information; for example, "food label" or "encyclopedia."

Answers to Questions

❶ A. _____

_____

B. _____

_____

C. _____

_____

D. _____

_____

❷ Item	❸ Composition	❸ Source
1.		
2.		
3.		
4.		
5.		
6.		
7.		
8.		

Results

Briefly describe what you discovered about the composition of the various items.

For example:

Kellogg's Sugar Smacks cereal contains vitamin C, which is called

sodium ascorbate.

_____

_____

_____

_____

_____

_____

_____

_____

_____

_____

_____

_____

Conclusions

State your conclusions based on the information you collected.

For example:

Many cereals contain sodium in the form of salt and vitamin C.

_____

_____

_____

_____

_____

_____

_____

_____

_____

_____

_____

_____

_____

Review

Define the following terms:

chemistry _____

_____

matter _____

_____

atoms (atomos) _____

_____

proton _____

_____

neutron _____

_____

electron _____

_____

nucleus _____

_____

electron cloud _____

_____

element _____

_____

atomic weight _____

_____

Experiment 2: Making marshmallow molecules Date: _____

Objective   To learn how atoms fit together by making marshmallow molecules

Materials

small, colored marshmallows
large marshmallows
toothpicks

Experiment

❶ Take several marshmallows of both sizes and several toothpicks.

❷ Make shapes from the marshmallows and toothpicks. First, form any number of links between marshmallows (i.e., put any number of toothpicks into each marshmallow). Draw the shapes below, noting the number of toothpicks in each marshmallow.

❸ Using new marshmallows, assign an "atom" to each of the marshmallows. The large marshmallows should be C, N, and O, and the small marshmallows should be H and Cl. Use the following "rules" for the number of toothpicks that can go into a marshmallow.

carbon – 4 toothpicks all pointing away from each other

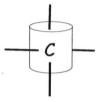

nitrogen – 3 toothpicks pointing downward

oxygen – 2 toothpicks pointing downward

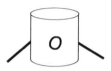

hydrogen and chlorine – 1 toothpick pointing in any direction

Cl or H

❹ Next, try to make the following molecules from your marshmallow atoms.

To make each molecule, follow the rules in step 3, then draw the shape of each molecule you make on the following chart.

H_2O :   This is one oxygen and two hydrogens.

NH_3:   This is one nitrogen and three hydrogens.

CH_4:   This is one carbon and four hydrogens.

CH_3OH: This is one carbon with three hydrogens and one oxygen attached. The oxygen has one hydrogen attached to it.

H_2O	NH_3
CH_4	CH_3OH

❺ Now, following the "rules" outlined in step 3 for the marshmallow molecules, make other "molecules." Make as many different shapes as you can without breaking the "rules." Draw your shapes below.

Conclusions

_____

_____

_____

_____

_____

_____

_____

_____

_____

_____

_____

_____

_____

_____

_____

_____

_____

Review

Define the following terms:

molecule _____

_____

bond _____

_____

shared electron bond _____

_____

unshared electron bond _____

_____

sodium chloride _____

_____

Answer the following questions:

How many bonds does hydrogen typically form? _____

How many bonds does carbon typically form? _____

How many bonds does nitrogen typically form? _____

How many bonds does oxygen typically form? _____

Draw the shape of a water molecule:

Experiment 3: Identifying chemical reactions   Date: _____

Objective   In this experiment we will try to identify a chemical reaction by observing the changes that occur when two solutions are added together.

Hypothesis   A chemical reaction can be identified by observing changes that occur in the course of the reaction.

Materials

baking soda
lemon juice
balsamic vinegar
salt (1-2 tbsp. dissolved in 1/2 cup of water)
egg whites
milk
several small jars
measuring cups and spoons
eye dropper

Experiment

❶ Look at the chart in the Results section. Write down all of the items (i.e., baking soda, lemon juice, balsamic vinegar, salt, egg whites, and milk) horizontally above each column.

❷ Now write the same list of items vertically down the left side of the grid, next to each row.

❸ There should be an item assigned to each column and to each row.

❹ In the boxes in the chart, record what you observe when the item listed in the column is mixed with the item in the corresponding row.

❺ Look especially for changes that indicate a chemical reaction has taken place. For example, look for bubbles, color change, or a precipitate.

❻ Ask your teacher for unknown solutions. When you mix them, try to determine whether a chemical reaction has taken place. Try to identify what the unknown solutions are.

Results

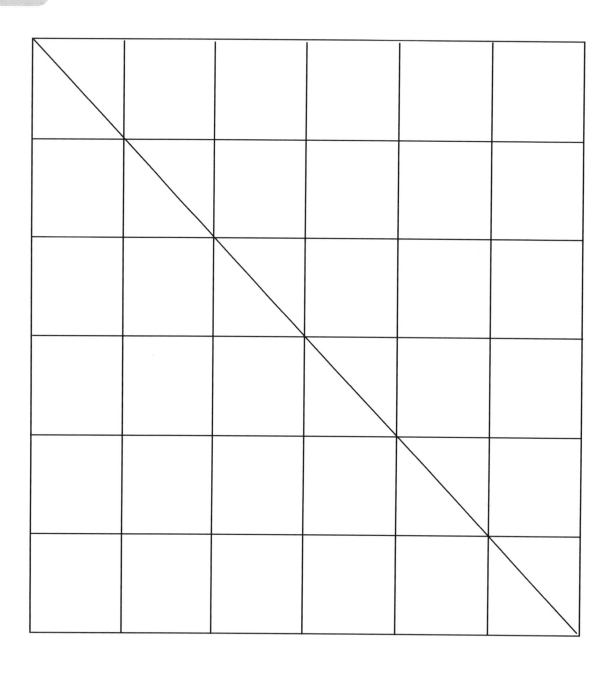

Results for unknown solutions

Descriptions:

❶ _____

_____

❷ _____

_____

Results when the two are mixed:

_____

_____

_____

What might they be?

_____

_____

_____

Conclusions

_____

_____

_____

_____

_____

_____

_____

_____

_____

_____

_____

_____

_____

_____

_____

_____

Review

What are the four types of chemical reactions?

_____

_____

_____

_____

Define the following terms:

chemical reaction _____

_____

combination reaction _____

_____

decomposition reaction _____

_____

displacement reaction _____

_____

exchange reaction _____

_____

spontaneous _____

_____

List four changes that can be observed when a chemical reaction occurs.

_____

_____

_____

_____

Experiment 4: Making an acid-base indicator   Date: _____

Objective _____

_____

Hypothesis _____

_____

Materials

one head of red cabbage   small jars
distilled water   white coffee filters
various solutions, such as: eye dropper
    ammonia   measuring cup
    vinegar   measuring spoons
    soda pop   marking pen
    milk   scissors
    mineral water   ruler
large saucepan

Experiment

❶ Take the whole head of red cabbage, and divide it into several pieces.

❷ Place three cups of distilled water in a pan, and bring the water to a boil. Place the cabbage in the boiling water and boil for several minutes.

❸ Remove the cabbage, and let the water cool. The water should be a deep purple color.

❹ Take one cup of the cabbage water to use in this experiment, and REFRIGERATE the rest for the next experiment.

❺ Cut the coffee filters into small strips about 2 cm wide and 4 cm long. Make at least 20.

❻ Using the eye dropper, put several drops of the cabbage water onto each of the filter papers, and allow them to dry. They should be slightly pink and uniform in color. If the papers are too light, more solution can be dropped onto them, and they can be dried again. These are your acid-base indicator (pH) papers.

❼ Label one of the jars "Control Acid," and place a tablespoon of vinegar into the jar. Add 5 tablespoons of distilled water. This is your *known* acid.

Label another jar "Control Base," and add a tablespoon of ammonia to the jar. Add 5 tablespoons of distilled water. This is your *known* base.

Put one tablespoon of each of the other solutions you have collected into separate jars, and add 2 to 5 tablespoons of distilled water to each.

❽ Carefully dip the pH paper into the "Control Acid." Look immediately at the pH paper for a color change, and record your results. Tape the pH paper in the space in the chart below in the "Control Acid" section.

❾ Carefully dip a new piece of pH paper into the "Control Base." Look immediately at the pH paper for a color change, and record your results. Tape the pH paper in the space below in the "Control Base" section.

❿ Now take new pieces of pH paper, and dip them into the other solutions you have made. Record your results. Tape the papers into the chart.

Results

pH Paper Sample	Name of Solution	Color of pH Paper	Acid/Base?
	Control Acid:		
	Control Base:		

Conclusions

_____

_____

_____

_____

_____

_____

_____

_____

_____

_____

_____

_____

_____

_____

_____

_____

_____

_____

Review

Define the following terms:

electrode _____

_____

pH meter _____

_____

litmus paper _____

_____

acid-base indicator _____

_____

acid-base reaction _____

_____

controls _____

_____

Answer the following questions:

What is the pH of a neutral solution? _____

What is the pH of an acidic solution? _____

What is the pH of a basic solution? _____

Is vinegar an acid or a base? _____

Is baking soda an acid or a base? _____

What is the chemical name for vinegar? _____

What is the chemical name for baking soda? _____

Experiment 5: Vinegar and ammonia in the balance: An introduction to titrations   Date: _____

Objective _____

_____

Hypothesis _____

_____

Materials

red cabbage indicator (from Experiment 4)
household ammonia
vinegar
large glass jar
measuring spoons
measuring cup

Experiment

❶ Measure 1/4 cup of vinegar, and put it in the glass jar.

❷ Add enough of the red cabbage indicator to get a deep red color.

❸ Using the measuring spoons, carefully add one teaspoon of the ammonia to the vinegar solution. Swirl gently, and record the color of the solution.

❹ Add another teaspoon of ammonia to the vinegar, and record the color of the solution.

❺ Keep adding ammonia to the vinegar, and record the color of the solution for every teaspoonful you add.

❻ When the color has changed from red to green, stop adding ammonia.

❼ Plot the data on the graph. The horizontal axis should be labeled "Teaspoons of Ammonia," and the vertical axis should be labeled "Color of Solution."

❽ For every teaspoon of ammonia added, mark the graph with a round dot corresponding to the color of the solution.

❾ When all of the data have been plotted, connect the dots.

Results

Number of Teaspoons	Color
One teaspoon	red
Two teaspoons	red

Graphing your data:

On the graph below, record the number of teaspoons (horizontal axis) corresponding to the color of the solution (vertical axis).

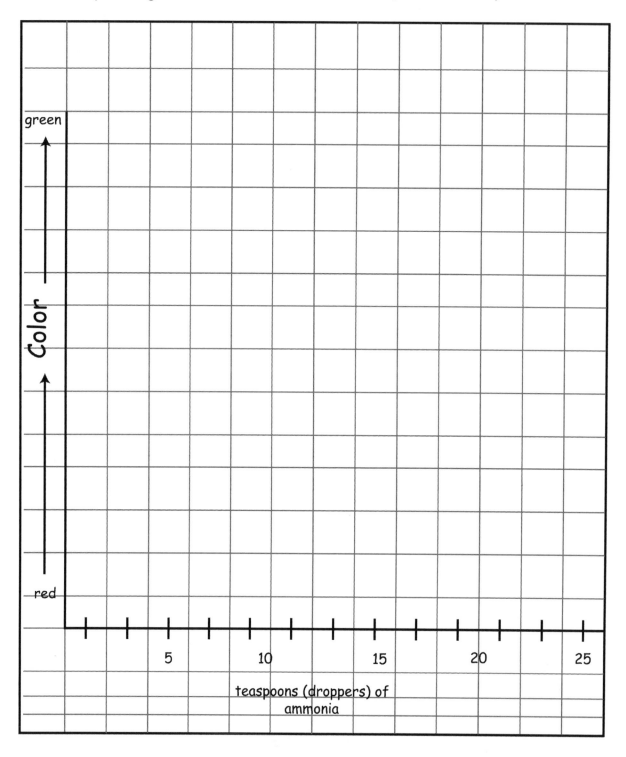

Conclusions

_____

_____

_____

_____

_____

_____

_____

_____

_____

_____

_____

_____

_____

_____

_____

_____

Review

Define the following terms:

neutralization reaction _____

_____

concentration _____

_____

concentrated _____

_____

dilute _____

_____

Glacial acetic acid _____

_____

acid indigestion _____

_____

titration _____

_____

axes (axis) _____

_____

Experiment 6: Mix it up!   Date: _____

Objective

_____

_____

Hypothesis

_____

_____

Materials

water   food coloring
ammonia   dish soap
vegetable oil   eye dropper
rubbing alcohol   measuring cup and
melted butter   measuring spoons
vinegar   marking pen
small jars (7 or more)

Experiment

Part I: See what mixes

❶ The grid in the Results section is labeled along the top and one side with the following terms: water, ammonia, vegetable oil, rubbing alcohol, melted butter and vinegar.

❷ Take out 6 small jars, and add 1/4 cup of each item to separate jars. Label the jars.

❸ Add a drop of food coloring to each jar.

❹ Using a clean jar each time, mix one tablespoon of an uncolored item with 1 tablespoon of a colored item. In the boxes on the next page, record whether or not the two items mix.

Results

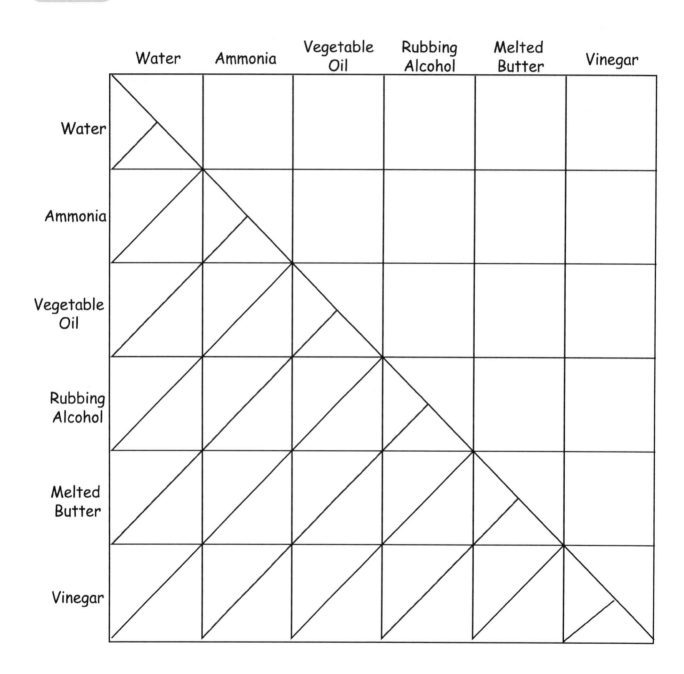

Part II: Soap, oil, and water

❶ Put 1/4 cup of water into a small glass jar. Add one drop of food coloring.

❷ Add 1 tablespoon of vegetable oil to the water.

❸ Mix the water and oil. Record your results.

❹ Add 1 tablespoon of liquid dish soap to the oil/water mixture.

❺ Mix thoroughly. Record your results.

❻ Add another tablespoon of liquid dish soap to the mixture, and mix thoroughly.

❼ Record your results.

Results

Oil + water _____

_____

Oil + water + 1T soap _____

_____

Oil + water + 2T soap _____

_____

Conclusions

_____

_____

_____

_____

_____

_____

_____

_____

_____

_____

_____

_____

_____

_____

_____

Review

Define the following terms:

mixture _____

_____

homogeneous _____

_____

heterogeneous _____

_____

dissolve _____

_____

Answer the following questions:

What does the phrase "like dissolves like" mean? _____

_____

_____

Name two molecules with charged ends. _____

_____

Name two molecules without charged ends. _____

_____

How does soap work? _____

_____

_____

Draw a micelle.

Experiment 7: Black is black?   Date: _____

Objective   _____

             _____

Hypothesis   _____

             _____

Materials

   ball point ink pens of various   cardboard shoe box
      colors, including black   tape
   rubbing alcohol   measuring cup
   coffee filters (white)   scissors
   several small jars   ruler

Experiment

❶ Pour 1/4 cup of alcohol into each of several small jars.

❷ Take each ink pen, and remove the thin plastic tube from the inside.

❸ Pull off the top or cut the end off the plastic tube.

❹ Take the tube and swirl the end of it in the alcohol. Make sure that some of the color gets dissolved in the alcohol, but don't let it get too colored.

❺ Cut the coffee filter paper into thin strips 1/4 to 1/2 inch wide and 5 to 6 inches long.

❻ Place the ends of the strips in the dissolved ink in the jars, and allow the alcohol to migrate upwards. It is OK for the strips to touch the sides of the glass jars, but the alcohol won't migrate past this point. It is better if you can suspend the strips in the alcohol without letting them touch the sides. To do this, tape the strips to the inside of a cardboard box, and suspend them in the glass jars.

❼ The colors in the ink will migrate up the absorbent strips. Let the strips sit in the alcohol overnight.

Results

Tape the strips of paper below. Write down each original ink color, and record the different colors that each is made of.

Orange Ink made of yellow and red						

Repeat the previous steps using a sample of an unknown ink. Try to determine the colors that make up the unknown ink sample by comparing your results with those of the previous samples.

Unknown

Color of the unknown ink:

_____

Conclusions

_____

_____

_____

_____

_____

_____

_____

_____

_____

_____

_____

_____

_____

_____

_____

_____

_____

_____

_____

Review

Define the following terms:

sieve _____

_____

filter _____

_____

filtration _____

_____

pores _____

_____

solid state _____

_____

gaseous state _____

_____

liquid state _____

_____

chromatography _____

_____

separation _____

_____

Experiment 8: Show me the starch!   Date: _____

Objective _____

_____

Hypothesis _____

_____

Materials

tincture of iodine [Iodine is VERY poisonous—DO NOT EAT any food
   items with iodine on them.]
a variety of raw foods, including:
   pasta
   bread
   celery
   potato
   banana
   other fruits
liquid laundry starch
absorbent white paper
eye dropper
cookie sheet
marking pen

Experiment

❶ Take several food items and place them on a cookie sheet.

❷ Using the eye dropper, put a small amount of liquid starch on a piece of absorbent paper, and label it "Control." Let it dry.

❸ Add a drop of iodine to the starch on the control paper. Record the color.

❹ Add iodine to each of the food items, and record the color.

❺ Compare the color on the "control" to the color of each food item.

❻ Note those food items that changed color and those that did not.

Results

Food Item	Color
Control	

Conclusions

_____

_____

_____

_____

_____

_____

_____

_____

_____

_____

_____

_____

_____

_____

_____

_____

_____

Review

Define the following terms:

nutrients _____

_____

carbohydrate _____

_____

monosaccharide _____

_____

disaccharide _____

_____

polysaccharide _____

_____

starch _____

_____

cellulose _____

_____

amylose _____

_____

amylopectin _____

_____

Experiment 9: Gooey glue   Date: _____

Objective   _____

             _____

Hypothesis   _____

             _____

Materials

    liquid laundry starch
    Elmer's white glue
    Elmer's blue glue (or another glue different from white glue)
    water
    2 small jars
    marking pen
    Popsicle sticks for stirring
    measuring spoons

Experiment

Part I

❶ Open the bottle of Elmer's white glue. Put a small amount on your fingertips. Note the color and consistency (sticky, dry, hard, soft) of the glue. Record your observations.

❷ Now look carefully at the liquid starch. Pour a small amount on your fingers or in a jar. Note the color and consistency of the starch. Record your observations.

❸ Take one of the jars, and put 4 tablespoons of water into it.

❹ Note the level of water in the jar, and draw a small line with a marker at the water level.

❺ Add another 4 tablespoons of water, and mark the water level with a marker.

❻ Pour the water out.

❼ Fill the jar to the first mark with Elmer's glue.

❽ Fill the jar to the second mark with liquid starch.

❾ Mix the glue and the starch with a Popsicle stick. Record any changes in consistency and color.

❿ Take the mixture out of the jar, and knead it with your fingers. Observe the consistency and color, and record your results.

Results

Observations for Elmer's white glue: _____

_____

_____

_____

Observations for liquid starch: _____

_____

_____

_____

Observations for mixture of Elmer's white glue and equal amount of liquid starch:

_____

_____

_____

_____

_____

_____

Part II

❶ Take another jar, and follow steps 3-6 in Part I of this experiment. This time, fill the jar to the first mark with the Elmer's blue glue or another glue that is different from the white glue.

❷ Add liquid starch to the second level.

❸ Mix.

❹ Record your observations.

Results

Observations for mixture of blue glue and liquid starch:

_____

_____

_____

_____

_____

_____

_____

_____

_____

_____

_____

_____

Conclusions

_____

_____

_____

_____

_____

_____

_____

_____

_____

_____

_____

_____

_____

_____

_____

_____

_____

Review

Define the following terms:

meros _____

_____

polymer _____

_____

monomer _____

_____

polyethylene _____

_____

vulcanization _____

_____

Experiment 10: Amylase action   Date: _____

Objective _____

_____

Hypothesis _____

_____

Materials

tincture of iodine [VERY POISONOUS—DO NOT EAT any food items that
   have iodine on them]
bread
timer   marking pen
wax paper   cup

Experiment

❶ Break the bread into several small pieces.

❷ Chew one piece for 30 seconds (use the timer), chew another piece for
   1 minute, and a third piece for as long as possible (several minutes).

❸ Each time, after chewing the bread, spit it onto a piece of wax paper.
   Using the marking pen, label the wax paper with the length of time the
   bread has been chewed.

❹ Take three small pieces of un-chewed bread, and place one next to each
   of the chewed pieces.

❺ Add a drop of iodine to each piece of bread, chewed and un-chewed.

❻ Record your observations.

❼ Take two more pieces of bread. Collect as much saliva from your mouth
   as you can (spit into a cup several times). Soak both pieces of bread in
   the saliva. Place one piece in the refrigerator, and leave the other piece
   at room temperature. Let them soak for 30 minutes.

❽ After 30 minutes add a drop of iodine to each. Record your results.

Results

Chewed Bread				Bread + Saliva 30 minutes	
30 seconds	1 minute	Several minutes	Un-chewed Bread	Refrigerated	Not Refrigerated

Conclusions

Review

Define the following terms:

protein _____

_____

amino acid _____

_____

peptide bond _____

_____

kinesin _____

_____

DNA _____

_____

nucleotide _____

_____

double helix _____

_____

DNA polymerase _____

_____

Draw a picture of kinesin.

What are the four bases that make up DNA?

_____   _____

_____   _____

What are the symbols for the four bases that make up DNA?

_____

7878370R0

Made in the USA
Charleston, SC
18 April 2011